IN ALL

A Return to the Drooling Ward

CHARLIE,
THANKS FOR YOUR
HELP WITH THIS, IT REALLY
MADE A DIFFERENCE!

Ed

ED DAVIS

ISBN: 0986069728
ISBN-13: 9780986069727
Library of Congress Control Number: 2014944529
The Wedgewood Press, Graton, CA

For Martha Martin
Mom, thanks for that nudge out the door

CONTENTS

FORWARD

In the summer of 1970 I entered the Psychiatric Technician training program at what was then Sonoma State Hospital in Eldridge, California, a place Jack London immortalized with his 1914 short story "*Told in the Drooling Ward*." The hospital was eighty years old when I arrived, I was seventeen. This is a work of fiction, so I have taken some liberties to serve the story. But the place and the people are just as I remember them, and will be familiar to anyone who worked in similar settings during that time when the old ways were still hanging on and the new had not yet taken hold.

Across this span of years it is natural to look back in judgment, even disbelief, at what was then considered normal; that's how we know we're making progress. We can intellectualize but not really understand and certainly not excuse the distorted behaviors and clouded judgments born of institutions; be they mental hospitals of fifty years ago, internment camps of seventy-five years ago, or workhouses of a hundred years ago.

How then, I wonder, will observers fifty years from now view our current social institutions? Will they harshly judge our treatment of the homeless, or disabled veterans, or the hundreds of thousands in our prisons? Will they wonder at our inability to deal with immigration and poverty? Will they simply not understand our political paralysis over gun rights, gay rights and abortion? Maybe. Hopefully, because that means we will have moved on, though only time will tell in what direction.

Whether it is a hospital ward, a prison cell, a political party or a point in time, the view from inside is different than from outside. What we observe every day shapes who we are and how we behave, so seeing both the outside <u>and</u> inside of things, though often uncomfortable, is vital.

This brief tale takes you inside a place that for all practical purposes no longer exists; it was beginning to change dramatically and for the better even as I left it in 1972. That's a good thing. But the types of pressures and rationalizations that spawned its creation in the first place, and colored the actions of those who worked there, are all around us still.

Ed Davis
June 26, 2014
Glen Ellen, California

CHAPTER ONE

THIS IS NOT a confession.

It seems to me that a genuine confession requires three things: sins, a need to confess them, and God. My sins, whether real or imagined, are plentiful enough. And I must feel a need to share them or I wouldn't be writing this, though what I'm doing feels more like remembering than confessing. Maybe that's all confession is, remembering without rationalizing. Do you suppose amnesiacs believe they are free of sin? Maybe.

But can there be confession without God in the mix? I don't think I believe in God, never have. Years ago a friend described me as looking for God in all things. I liked the sound of that, still do; looking is not quite not- believing. If I did intend this to be a confession, who would I be talking to, I wonder? And would there be absolution waiting for me at the end?

Maybe.

———∞∞∞———

IT WAS AN accident, or at least an oversight, that I was there at all. In that way I had more in common with the thirty five hundred inmates at The State Home for the Feeble Minded than most. Many still called them inmates then, or at least the bughousers did. But "patients" had recently become preferred so that's the term I'll use. In succeeding decades "patients" would be replaced by "residents", then "clients." But in 1970 they were still inmates to the old-timers who worked there. At age seventeen I was probably the youngest trainee they had ever accepted, a year younger than the law required. Somehow they missed my age on the application; an accident.

Accidents of nurture or nature or neglect had placed most of the patients there. An umbilical cord twisted improperly, a wrong medication prescribed, an extra chromosome or a missing gene. For nearly a century they'd been coming, sent by parents who loved but couldn't care for them; parents who didn't want them; parents who were afraid of them. Sent as infants by doctors who advised their families to forget that they'd ever existed. Referred by schools who lacked the means or skills to educate them, communities who feared their behavior and jails that needed the space.

Boys and girls, men and women, young and old were sent to "The State Home" to live their lives apart. It was simply understood that they needed a place where the abnormal was normal, where their unusual needs could be met, where they would be safe. All that was true. It was equally true that their separate world was created as much for our peace of mind and protection as for their safety.

And in that separate world there was very little to protect them from us.

I first learned about it in my junior year of high school. A biology teacher with a flair for the unconventional took a small group of us there on a field trip. It was a couple of valleys over, less than an hour's journey away but a place I'd never been to or heard of. Driving onto the grounds was like entering a college campus. Tile roofed buildings were scattered among oaks and elms, well tilled flower gardens bordered manicured lawns, all of it with a picturesque mountain backdrop.

We spent that first afternoon in a quaint meeting hall with a group of older patients in wheelchairs. We sang songs, ate snacks and made crepe paper and pipe cleaner flowers. Many of them could speak---some clearly, others less so, though they all knew how to laugh. They were dressed in street clothes like the regular folks we might see around town. Some of their bodies were twisted a bit, some had withered limbs. Some bobbed their heads in jerks and lurches as we maneuvered them through wheelchair square dancing on the worn wooden floor.

They thanked us when we left, grasping and shaking our hands if they could, and saying or nodding goodbye. Then staff members in hospital whites appeared and rolled the patients back to their cottages. That's what they called them, cottages.

We drove back to our lives.

A big part of my life in those days was a job at the feed store in town. It was a couple of hours after school, more on the weekends, lifting feed sacks, loading hay bales and selling the occasional bit of hardware somebody might need around the farm. I had noticed the customer before, even waited on him a few times. A big guy---probably in his forties, probably delivered milk for a dairy I guessed, judging from his white uniform. He never did buy feed, though. Every few weeks he'd go to our hardware section and buy an electric cattle prod, sometimes more than one. They came in two-battery, four-battery, and six-battery models, and looked like flashlights. Only instead of a light bulb on the business end they had two electrodes half an inch apart; press the button and an electric arc would jump between them. Press them against the hide of a thousand pound balky steer and it would jump right out of the way. This man in white favored the two bat-tery size.

I had forgotten this incident until an old friend from the feed store reminded me of it not long ago. I don't know what we thought the customer was doing with all those cattle prods, if it even crossed our minds. I don't know if I was curious, suspicious or just making conversation when he came up to buy more that day. I imagine I must have said something like, "You sure go through a lot of these." And I imagine him saying in return, "They're not all for me. I just pick them up for my buddies over at The State Home."

I said in the beginning that this isn't a confession. It also isn't about heroes and villains or good and evil. That would be too easy, and none of this is easy. I don't remember what I did in the feed store that day. My friend claims that they almost had to pull me off the guy. I wish I could tell you, to tell myself, that it was some sort of moral, righteous reaction. I would love to believe that it was intentional, or at least conscious. But I don't think so.

If there is a single heroic act on my part anywhere in this tale that may have been it. And I don't remember it at all. I was sixteen, and that was forty-five years ago.

Chapter Two

I APPLIED TO The State Home's Psychiatric Technician training program the summer after I graduated from high school. I could have played football at the JC, or worked full time at the feed store. I could have just hung out, my mom probably would have put up with that for a while. But she clipped a "Career Opportunity" entry from the classifieds one day and handed it to me, knowing I'd do it. Since that first volunteer trip I'd gone back to The State Home more than once, sometimes with friends, sometimes on my own. I'd never been inside one of the cottages, though I now understood that insiders called them wards. And I'd always worked with that same group of patients, knew many of them by name, and some of them knew me.

To qualify for the program you had to take a test, you had to be at least eighteen years old, and you had to be willing to work for two hundred dollars per month for a year. The test questions were simple English and math; if one pint of bleach in a gallon of water will mop 100 square feet of floor, how many quarts of bleach do you need for 400 square feet? The money was terrible, but it was something. As for the age? The program started in August; I didn't turn eighteen until the end of September. Maybe they overlooked it intentionally. I suspect they just missed it.

The entrance exam was held in the cavernous old gymnasium on the grounds; several dozen of us lined up at long tables with our answer books and our pencils. Do you remember the moment when you first realized you were no longer in high school? For me it was right then, with a woman my mother's age struggling over the test to my right, and a guy with Navy tattoos and a missing tooth doing the same to my left. There were ashtrays on the tables, most in use, and an industrial sized urn of coffee against the back wall. The proctors walking the floor were in nurse's uniforms, and had fist-sized bundles of keys riding heavily on their hips.

Our acceptance letters told us where and when to report, and where to buy our trainee uniforms; pale green smocks and white pants for the men, green knee-length smocks of the same color for the women. Regular ward personnel mostly wore whites; hospital workers in the kitchens and laundry wore khakis; doctors, administrators and volunteers usually wore civilian clothes. There were eighteen hundred staff in all, too many to know on sight, so the uniforms served as an instant means of identification, and of rank. Our green smocks placed us a short rung above the patients.

When I left home to begin my training I could not have known that I was embarking on two new lives, not one. There was the life that had to do with a place to live, a car, girlfriends and visits back home. This story is not about that life. This story is about the other life I began that summer on the sixteen hundred acres of the State Home for the Feeble Minded. I was one of almost six thousand patients, staff and volunteers who populated its parallel, invisible universe. Others made that journey with me but you won't find their names here. This is my story, not theirs, and I have no right to speak for them.

I will speak of the patients. I will use their names. They are gone now, all gone.

They were dead to most of the world even then.

———⟡———

A TRAINING GROUP consisted of thirty trainees, and a new group started every three months. In that way it was like high school again, only compressed into a single year. Unlike high school, except for our green smocks my group had almost nothing in common. Ranging in ages from seventeen to well over fifty we could have been plucked at random off the street; a widow, a conscientious objector, a merchant seaman, a single mom. Some had college degrees; others had barely graduated from twelfth grade. A few, like me, were there by chance as much as choice. Most were there because a licensed Psych Tech could earn good money, and they hoped they could hang on for a year until the real paychecks started rolling in. Some wanted to be nurses, even doctors, and this was a place to start. For others it was just a place to be.

Our days over the next year would be split evenly between class time, for which we would earn the college credits required for a license, and work time, for which we would earn our meager monthly stipend. Instructional units were ten weeks long, focusing on the various skills we would need as Psych Techs. Our work wards, referred to as "clinical wards," would change every ten weeks, and were supposed to align, at least roughly, with those skill sets.

"A very innovative system," we were told on our first morning's orientation. Then we each received a map of the grounds, our ward assignment for the first ten weeks, and instructions to go check in. We would work there through the morning and report back after lunch.

Simple.

I had driven in the grounds a few times over the previous year, and seen patients shuffling in slow groups, or standing and waving, or sitting on benches and staring at the ground or at nothing. But except for those few I'd volunteered with I had never actually walked among them myself; none of the trainees had.

When I think back on The State Home now, and I think of it often, it appears to me not as one place but as many, each layered on top of the others. I had seen one layer, perhaps the top, as a volunteer. Now, as I walked to my first ward assignment, I was seeing another.

A group of female patients was on the sidewalk ahead coming my way, a white-clad Psych Tech ushering them along. Some walked, some staggered; others seemed almost to bounce with big lurching steps that propelled them upwards as much as forwards. They wore colorful but shapeless nylon shifts, tennis shoes with white socks sagging around their ankles, and expressions ranging from blank to beatific. The Tech nodded as they passed, and though he said nothing most of the women in his group did seem to be speaking, or mumbling, or moaning. They took no particular notice of me as I walked by.

A large fellow in overalls did notice as I approached, walked up to me and extended his hand. He pumped it up and down rapidly a few times before I could grasp it. "Meet you," he said, and turned away as quickly as he'd come.

My first work ward was part way up the hill, behind the huge laundry facility. A group of patients were pushing bulging canvas laundry tubs from the back of a truck, up a ramp and through the steaming doors, all under the stern gaze of another patient, a "Detail" who was obviously in charge. Details, I soon learned, did or supervised most of the physical work at The State Home. Among the patient population they had the most freedom, and the most power. This one barked a string of orders. I couldn't understand him but the members of his crew clearly did, some actually flinching as his words fell on them like blows.

I was assigned to a ward for adolescent boys, and found the shift supervisor, a middle aged man with glasses and thinning hair, in a small office just inside the main door. "We're a modern ward," he explained as he walked me around. "All the Techs wear street clothes, except on night shift, and the patients are organized into teams by ability." I could hear activity outside, but the ward itself was quiet and empty. "You will be assigned to The Thunderbirds, which are mostly high functioning morons. The Falcons are mostly imbeciles, The Ravens mostly mongoloids with a few cretins. We're not supposed to use names like moron and imbecile anymore, and officially we don't. But calling them educable or trainable doesn't make them any smarter."

This ward, like most I would come to know at The State Home, had a big day hall, a dining hall, dormitories with adjoining bathrooms, and an isolation wing off to one side. Built decades earlier of stone and stucco, the buildings had cement floors, open-raftered ceilings and narrow barred windows set deep in thick walls. "The Thunderbirds are our highest functioning team, so we've turned the isolation wing into bedrooms for them," my guide explained, walking me down a hallway with a series of tiny cells off to one side, each heavy wooden door swung open to reveal a low hospital bed neatly made, a throw rug and not much more. "Since Thorazine there hasn't been much need for isolation cells," he said. "Inmates used to hate lockup, now we use these rooms as a reward. If a Thunderbird screws up too much we put him in the dorms for a while and he has to earn his way back."

My tour ended in the day yard, a chain-link enclosed asphalt patch the size of a small basketball court. The Thunderbirds, Falcons and Ravens were all there; sitting or rocking or staring up at the sky through the fencing that sealed off the top of the space as well as the walls. Three Techs, one for each team, were sitting in the shade off to one side. We shook hands, exchanged names, and the supervisor left us.

Ducktail was in charge of The Thunderbirds on day shift. No, his name wasn't Ducktail, and no, I'm not changing it to protect him. He was in his thirties, he had jet black hair worn in a ducktail, and his real name is his business. Within the confines of The State Home there was a culture of classification, by uniform for the staff, by syndrome for the patients. Within the confines of this chronicle if I classify some of the players by their hair styles, that's no less than the institution was doing to all of us.

"You'll do fine here," Ducktail was telling me, "this is easy duty, not like the back wards. With these high-grade kids toileting and feeding is no big deal, and you won't have to get rough with them unless they get rough with you. Robert, come here," he called to a boy who was standing a few yards away and staring at the sun through his wavering fingers. "Robert's a high-grade boy, aren't you Robert?"

"High-grade boy," Robert answered. He was in his early teens, with acne and a crew cut, and hands that never really stopped moving. "Coffee?" he said, not looking at Ducktail or me exactly, but at a spot somewhere above and behind us.

"Sure, coffee," Ducktail said. "First I need to choke you out." He took Robert by the shoulders, stood behind him and wrapped an arm around his neck, his elbow forming a "V' at the boy's Adam's apple. "One of these guys gives you a hard time, this sets them straight," he said, applying pressure until Robert went limp in his arms.

Robert was a Thunderbird, as were Jimmy and Tyrone, and a handful of other boys that I would spend my mornings with over the next ten weeks. As a trainee I was just an extra set of hands in a routine where my hands were not much needed. The boys did most of the work, and the medications did most of the supervising. There was Dilantin for seizures, and many boys had the enlarged gums and facial hair that came with it. But it was Thorazine that made the ward run smoothly, Thorazine and coffee

The Thorazine was doled out in little paper cups several times a day, along with a smattering of other pills and supplements. The coffee, coal black and scalding hot, was served from a huge metal urn in the dining hall. Thorazine didn't knock the boys out completely, but it came close. Maybe their thirst for coffee was a natural counteraction to that. Whatever the reason, it was highly prized; given as a reward for good behavior and withheld as punishment. When Robert snuck away from us in the day room one morning it was only a few minutes before we found him in the dining hall, his head under the coffee urn, his mouth wide open beneath the steaming spigot. Ducktail told me they'd seen the boy do it many times. In spite of the burns to his cheeks, tongue and throat, he would clearly do it again whenever he got the chance.

For Tyrone it was running that he could not get enough of. In the day yard that first morning, while the other boys mostly sat or rocked, Tyrone ran. Back and forth he went, between the chain-link walls, back and forth. I had finished my morning shift, eaten lunch at the employee cafeteria down the hill, and was walking to class when Tyrone came running past me. Ducktail had been walking his Thunderbirds to school when Tyrone broke away and sprinted off.

I called after the boy. When he didn't respond I gave chase, finally tackling him on an expanse of green lawn in front of the administration building. He didn't struggle when I had him on the ground, and when Ducktail and the others came up minutes later he rejoined them without complaint.

"He might have made it up into the hills this time," Ducktail said, motioning to the sweep of mountain that formed The State Home's western border. "There's creeks and caves, even a lake. We've lost a few up there over the years, but usually they find their way back if we don't find them first."

"And those that you don't find, or don't come back on their own?"

Ducktail shrugged, then herded his Thunderbirds on toward class.

CHAPTER THREE

OUR FIRST WEEK was a survey of the year to come, one day devoted to each of the five subject areas we would be studying in the coming months. It was like a guided tour through a house of wonders.

Newborns and babies, and there were many, were cared for in a special nursery facility, our first stop. It had cribs, and basinets, and the most modern medical equipment to be found anywhere on the grounds. And within those cribs and basinets, wonders. In one crib a little hydrocephalic girl, her head three times the size of her body, her skull so thin that the beam of a flashlight passed right through it. And in the next crib the opposite condition; a child with a head the size of a softball. There were cleft palates so large they seemed to completely erase noses and mouths. There were organs developing in glistening bundles outside of bodies, rather than in. Some infants appeared to be physically perfect, yet behind their eyes was absolutely nothing. "Normal Child Development" would be our first instructional unit. The supervisor in charge told us with obvious pride that collected in this one place, in this one nursery, were more examples of abnormal child development than anywhere else in the country.

The next day we saw a sampling of the nursing practices we'd be called upon to use, some of them demonstrated by the patients themselves. Nasal feeding tubes were common on the bed wards; we saw them inserted and removed. Colostomy bags were changed, blood pressures read and temperatures taken. We were introduced to a young girl who demonstrated the proper way to insert and remove a Foley catheter. Her name, Lisa, had been popular a decade earlier when she was born, and Thalidomide had been a popular anti-morning sickness drug at the time. Lisa had no arms, just hands that seemed to grow out of her shoulders like flippers. But her legs were long and loosely jointed, and using her toes like fingers she expertly inserted the rubber tube in her own urethra, chatting casually with us as we watched.

On our third day of orientation we were guided through what amounted to a living textbook of the syndromes associated with mental retardation. An older male patient with acromegaly, his brow, jaw and hands like those of Frankenstein's monster, sat doing crafts with his micro cephalic friend, whose head tapered to a point above his neck. We saw faces half covered with the port-wine stains of Surge-Weber syndrome, or fully obscured by the wart-like growths of neurofibromatosis. The almond shaped eyes and round faces of Down's syndrome were plentiful, as were the twisted bodies and lurching gestures of those with cerebral palsy. PKU patients were characterized by their fair skin and musty odor, while those with the elfin facial features of William's syndrome had bright eyes and beguiling smiles. Children with cretinism looked like pixies, adults with damaged or missing pituitary glands, giants. And Melvin Santini, one of The State Home's autistic savants, could tell you what day of the week you were born on if you gave him your birthdate, could play any piece of music on the piano having heard it just once, but could not walk more than three steps in a row without kicking himself in the butt with his own heel.

Any community of thirty-five hundred people would have its own hospital, and on our fourth day of orientation we toured The State Home's; an imposing three-story Gothic structure with turrets, marble floors, and an ancient elevator operated by an equally ancient Detail in bellman's livery. We saw patients being prepared for tonsillectomies and appendectomies; we saw broken limbs being set in casts. We toured the operating room, with a stern caution not to touch anything. The chief of surgery explained to us that while the procedures they performed might sound familiar, with these patients they were anything but. "When a body has been twisted by cerebral palsy or confinement to bed for decades, internal organs are often not where we expect them to be, so each new operation is like a journey into the unknown. Surgical interns find training experiences with us that are not available anywhere else," he said, "and because of our unique patient population, groundbreaking research has been conducted in this hospital for over fifty years."

Our last day of orientation took us to a pair of behavior wards, one for adolescents, another for adults. At the first, new behavior modification techniques were being used to shape and guide every aspect of the young patients' lives in an effort to make them more self-sufficient. Basic daily tasks were analyzed and broken down into the smallest possible steps---brushing teeth, using a fork, buttoning a shirt---and each successful step was rewarded with praise and an M&M. This, we were told, was a pioneering approach to training the mentally retarded, and the early results were far exceeding expectations. Yet no one knew if the effects would last once the M&M's were withdrawn.

On the adult behavior ward there were no such innovative techniques in use. These patients had lived much of their lives within the institution. Catatonics sat or stood statue-like, seemingly unaware of their surroundings, their limbs motionless unless repositioned by staff. Lobotomy patients drifted around the ward like ghost ships that had slipped their moorings, their gazes blank, their heads adorned with semi-circular scars. And the schizophrenics paced, or talked to invisible companions, or cowered in the corners. This was a ward without decoration or pretense; bare walls, hard benches, and the hard stares of large, white-clad attendants watching every move.

"Our job here is to keep them from harming themselves or each other," the Tech in charge explained. One of the pacing schizophrenics overheard, moved closer, and stared for a moment at each of us, his red-rimmed eyes unblinking. "Johnny," the Tech spoke a single word of warning and the patient backed away, his eyes locked on those of the supervisor, his look not of fear but of absolute hatred.

CHAPTER FOUR

THERE WAS A rhythm to The State Home that we trainees quickly fell into; half days on the wards, half days in class, weekends left to our lives outside the place though never really away from its influence. Many of us would have gone hungry without it. After taxes our take home pay was scarcely enough to cover rent, let alone buy groceries. The hospital had its own central bakery, producing wax paper-wrapped loaves of coarse dry bread in staggering quantities every day. Ducktail, when the ward charge wasn't watching, slipped me a loaf, and a pound of institutional grade butter to go with it. "Everybody does it," he assured me, "and for you trainees they must expect it, how else could you eat on what they pay you? Just make sure you don't get caught."

The food was mostly awful, but edible. We would wrap it in jackets, tuck into car trunks; stash it behind a bush for pickup after shift. The State Home provided colorless green beans and syrup-soaked peach halves in gallon cans, pasty oatmeal and pulpy orange juice on the wards in the morning, even the occasional tasteless sheet cake left over from a special occasion. And though the price was right, it wasn't altogether free. Rather, it was the cost of admission to yet another layer of the place; one where the rules were largely ignored, and where looking the other way and keeping your mouth shut was not just expected but required.

Did everyone take food or the occasional piece of clothing from the donation bins, or toilet paper or toothpaste?

Probably not.

I hope not, but I certainly did.

WHEN MY FIRST ten weeks came to an end I was transferred away from The Thunderbirds and onto a ward full to overflowing with old women in muumuus and creaking wooden wheelchairs. The day hall was like a slow motion bumper car ride of clashing chairs and cackling old ladies. My class hours were spent learning about sphygmomanometers, giving practice injections to navel oranges, and administering first aid to a mechanical dummy. My ward hours were spent putting women my grandmother's age on and off the toilet, cleaning vomit from whiskered chins, combing lice from balding scalps, and washing my hands; constantly washing my hands.

"This ward is a bowl of sepsis," the charge nurse, an anxious woman with red, chafed fingers told me on the first day, then she guided me to a deep sink with paddle-handled faucets and showed me the source of the chafing. "The water needs to be hot enough to hurt," she said, opening the valve with her elbow, "the soap strong enough to sting," she squeezed a foul smelling liquid into her hands, "and if you aren't using a scrubber, you are wasting your time and mine." Then she took a nail brush and attacked her fingers is if she feared them, which she clearly did. Minutes later she handed me the brush, then stood back with arms crossed and instructed me, step by step, in how to do exactly the same.

Over the weeks that followed, though I never took a blood pressure, never gave an injection, and was never called upon to administer first aid, I washed my hands countless times, more out of fear of the charge nurse than of infection or illness. She expected to see her staff at the deep sink several times an hour, and was quick with a reprimand if she didn't.

I remember almost nothing else about those ten weeks; not the other staff, not the patients as individuals, not even the ward routine. The place smelled of bleach and the deeper, thicker odors it was trying to cover; that I recall. And the old women, though never physically threatening, disturbed me in a way that I could not name then, and am only beginning to understand now.

While The Thunderbirds looked fairly normal their actions were anything but, and that made them easier to accept somehow. By contrast those old ladies in their chairs, though disheveled, strangely dressed and crowded together like penned cattle, mostly acted like old women

I'd been around my whole life. The State Home gave them everything they needed; everything but dignity. I think it was that absence that made me uncomfortable.

Did I befriend any of those women, or have anything resembling relationships with them? I don't think so. I don't think I knew how.

Relationships would come later.

CHAPTER FIVE

"TAKE CARE OF my girl," Ponytail was saying as he stood beside the crib with me. His girl's name was Michelle, and she had been his case study a year earlier when he was still a trainee. Now he was a licensed Tech assigned to the hospital as a surgical assistant. But he still came back to visit her regularly, and the charge nurse had asked him to make the introduction. For the next ten weeks she would be my case study. "They don't believe she understands anything," he said, stroking her amazingly thin hair, "but they're full of shit. Look in those baby blues and tell me she doesn't understand."

We had learned about sunset eyes in class, and the conditions that can cause them, and I'd seen several examples in the nursery during orientation. But this was different. Michelle was not a baby. Her chart, the first I'd been allowed to examine as a trainee, said she was seven years old, and it told her story in bleak clinical detail. Born with hydrocephaly, she'd had a shunt installed to relieve spinal fluid pressure when she was less than a year old. But it soon failed, as did the next and the next. With each passing month her cranial plates separated more and more until finally, by the time a successful shunt was implanted, her head had grown to the size of a ripe watermelon.

"You pump her shunt here," Ponytail explained, guiding my fingers to bumps under Michelle's skin, just behind her ear. "Pump it twenty times an hour, one finger then the other, and make sure you feel the bumps spring back so we know it isn't clogged. They say it doesn't matter anymore, but screw 'em."

Ponytail was in his mid-twenties, wore wire rimmed glasses with dark lenses night and day, and was said to be a good weed connection for those who could afford it. I'd spoken to him a few times and seen him around the grounds, mostly at the cafeteria, mostly checking out the young female trainees for possible conquests. Though I did not know him, nothing in our brief previous encounters had inclined me to like him, or prepared me for his tenderness at the cribside.

"Like hell she doesn't know," he said, leaning down close to her, taking off his glasses and smiling. "Just look at those eyes."

When he was gone and I was alone with her I did look, closely and for a long time. Her eyes were the brightest blue, and set in a complexion so smooth and taut as to seem almost doll like. Her face was small, petite really. It was only above her wide, downy eyebrows that it started to change. What should have been a forehead was instead a sweep of drum-tight alabaster skin ballooning out and up eight inches or more, then curving back to form a gourd-like dome almost two feet in length. Her scalp was a roadmap of blood vessels, brightly colored and so near the surface you could see them pulsing, her filament-fine hair just sparsely scattered wisps.

A set of wedged foam blocks kept her head upright, and a crocheted cap, probably from a volunteer, adorned the back half of her skull to help keep it warm, and I think perhaps to make it look less strange. Below her petite chin was an equally petite body, more like that of a two year old than a seven year old. Most of the patients in the sixty-some cribs around us wore plain white hospital shifts; Michelle had a flowered nightie with little bows. And a smiling baby doll was in the crib with her, propped watchfully in a corner. Its eyelids could roll closed if it was laid on its back, but Michele's never would. The skin was stretched so tight above them that even in sleep her eyes were always open.

Michelle was one of two special patients assigned to me on this rotation. In addition to our other duties around the ward, each trainee was to devote particular attention to our two case studies; to feed, bathe and change them, to practice appropriate techniques we were learning in class, to observe and chart. My second patient was a girl named Baby. Her full name, when I looked in her records, was Baby Girl Smith. Admitted when she was only days old she had suffered terrible seizures right from birth. Her parents, on their doctor's advice, and given her up to The State Home, assured that she would live no more than a few weeks. That was thirty years earlier, and though the seizures never really abated Baby had refused to die.

Like many of the patients on this ward, all of whom had been confined to cribs their entire lives, Baby was "Pancaked." I don't think the term appeared in any medical book, but when teaching us about range of motion therapy in class our instructor made it clear that "Pancaking" was what happened if range of motion didn't. Bed sores, atrophied muscles, feeding problems, constipation; all were consequences of prolonged bed rest, all were common at the State Home, and all could be addressed with proper care. But when patients stayed in the same semi-fetal position, not for days and weeks but for months and years, their joints slowly solidified. Eventually, like pancakes, they lay flattened on their sides, unable to roll over or flex their arms and legs more than a few inches even during seizures.

Baby had cerebral palsy, and what her chart called, "brain dysfunction of undifferentiated origin," a catchall diagnosis applied to many of the patients at The State Home. Her body, unlike Michelle's, had grown to full size, though her limbs seemed impossibly thin; really just skin stretched over bone. Dressed in a simple white hospital gown, she seemed to be all knees and elbows, a coarse cloth diaper twisted between her scissored, petrified legs. Straight brown hair hung over her forehead, and large brown eyes looked out from a face drawn and distorted by decades of convulsions. On Michelle's face and in Michelle's eyes I wanted to see recognition, and wasn't sure that I did. On Baby's I saw recognition immediately and wished that I didn't.

Our routine on this ward was a mix of industrial efficiency and close but cold physical contact. Like many cottages at The State Home this one was seriously over crowded; sixty cribs crammed into each of three day halls for a total of a hundred and eighty patients that had to be fed, changed, and bathed all by just a handful of Techs and the three of us trainees assigned there. Bathing was Tuesdays and Fridays, and took place between morning and mid-day feeding. Patients were lifted from their cribs, loaded three to a gurney and whisked away to the central shower where they were stripped, sprayed and scrubbed. Still on the gurney, naked and dripping, they were whisked back to their day rooms, dried, dressed in clean gowns and returned to their newly remade cribs, all in a matter of minutes.

Feeding was just as efficient. Food in any rec-
ognizable form was nowhere to be found on this
ward. None of these patients could feed themselves, some lacked teeth and many lacked the
ability to swallow without gagging. "Modified
Soft" was the diet that most received. Delivered
in trucks from the central kitchen and doled out
on stainless steel divided trays, it consisted of
mechanically premasticated portions of meat,
vegetables, fruit and starch that were only iden-
tifiable by their colors; brown, green, yellow and
white. Those patients who could swallow were
fed several rapid tablespoons full, followed by a
few gulps of water and a wipe down. Patients who
couldn't swallow received their meals via large
plastic syringes and flexible tubes that passed
through their noses and into their stomachs. It
was faster than spoon feeding, and the injection
of water at the end cleaned the tube and made it
ready for the next meal.

Even more efficient was the experimental
feeding system being tested on several patients.
This was the height of the space age. An all-liquid
diet had been developed for consumption in a
weightless environment, and though rejected

by astronauts it seemed like a natural fit for those confined to beds for prolonged periods. No chewing was required, there was very little waste, and the troublesome digestive issues that could be problematic in a space capsule or a crib were kept to a minimum.

Digestive issues, constipation chief among them, were a constant on the ward. Most patients received a precautionary stool softener with their daily meds, and suppositories were prescribed on a regular basis for many. When those measures didn't work soap suds enemas were employed, yet those frequently failed leaving patients impacted and in danger of intestinal injury. At that point, in an act of stark physical intimacy, we would clear the blockage by hand; a process better imagined than described.

Just as intimate, though in an entirely different way, were the range of motion and brushing and icing therapies we practiced on our case study patients every day. Range of motion involved taking limbs, some that had been frozen in place for years, and carefully extending, rotating and flexing them, slowly trying to regain some of what had been lost to inaction and atrophy. The trick was to move a limb to its point of resistance in a given direction, then go just a little farther so that over time normal range might be restored. Michelle's body, remarkably, was not rigid at all, perhaps owing to the extra attention of Techs like Ponytail over the years. Her limbs gave almost no resistance, and could easily be moved. With her the challenge was rotating her whole body as a unit. She required frequent turning to avoid bedsores. A careless rotation of her enormous head independent of her torso, or the other way around, would have broken her neck easily.

Baby, by contrast, had lost virtually all normal range of motion in her limbs. They were locked in half flexed positions, legs tightly scissored together, one arm across her chest, the other bent at her side. Any attempt to move them more than an inch or two in any direction was met first with a look of fear, and then with a whimper escalating to a howl as the point of resistance was reached and exceeded. Our instructions were to push past that resistance point or else no progress would be made. The afternoon that a trainee working a few cribs over from me pushed a little too far, the sound of her case study's arm breaking echoed through the ward like a branch snapping in the forest.

Where my range of motion sessions were clearly a torment to Baby, my efforts at brushing and icing therapy produced the opposite reaction. The simple acts of chewing and swallowing normally had either never been mastered by many of the patients, or had been lost to them over the years. Tongue control, something we take for granted, was also a challenge for many. By gently stimulating the cheeks, lips and tongue with alternating strokes from a soft brush and a smooth ice cube it was thought that dormant nerve endings could be awakened; a first step toward gaining normal function. Baby, who had nothing approximating actual speech, could make a variety of sounds that communicated her meaning perfectly. The brush, when applied to her cheeks, elicited noises that bore no resemblance to any laughter I had ever heard, yet they were clearly just that. And when I applied the ice cube to her lips, tracing the seizure-twisted perimeter of her mouth around and around, the look in her eye and low tones from her throat conveyed a state approaching ecstasy.

Michelle's mouth was perfectly formed, and as the ice cube moved over her bow shaped lips her jaw would start to work and her tongue begin to thrust, exactly as hoped. Unlike most of the patients on this ward she had teeth, and though she would never feed herself it did seemed possible that one day she might use them to eat a diet more substantial than Modified Soft. Occasionally while I was gently brushing her cheek Michelle would speak a word or two; very soft, very clear, and not related to anything at all. I would write the words in her chart, and could see that others had been doing so for some time. There was no indication that she understood the words, or even that she had been taught to parrot them as some cruel trick. Rather, it was as though a few stray utterances had somehow filtered through her paper thin skull, become trapped inside her extraordinary head, and occasionally escaped through those petite lips.

Did she know what she was saying, or where she was, or understand what was going on around her as Ponytail had insisted? After ten weeks of spending a few hours a day at her crib side; feeding her, bathing her, even taking her outside in a stroller a time or two, I convinced myself that she did. I couldn't look into those eyes that never closed and not believe they didn't see, didn't communicate, though I had no idea what. Perhaps it was the mystery of not knowing that made her so appealing and attracted such unusual affection from the ward staff.

Baby Girl Smith attracted no such affection. She was not easy to look at or to care for, and there was no mystery at all about her.

After ten weeks at her crib side I also had no doubt that she knew exactly what was going on.

Chapter Six

Life outside the wards went on much as it would in any small town, unfolding in the rhythmic rituals of work, school, and socializing. During my lunch hours when the weather was mild I had fallen into the habit of sitting with a group of quiet, contemplative older men who daily staked out a row of fading metal lawn chairs near the cafeteria. Residents of The State Home since well before I was born, these men said little even amongst themselves, and rarely said anything to me. But I was welcome as long as a chair was open. Together we would sit and watch the comings and goings of the place.

Among the thirty five hundred patients there were many like Baby and Michelle who rarely left their cribs, and virtually never left their cottages.

Others, like my lunchtime companions, seemed to have the run of the grounds and could often be seen unescorted or in the company of friends as they went about their daily routines. Particularly high functioning patients were frequently tapped to be Details and given duties on the wards, in the kitchen or the laundry. Mario, a large, round-faced man who often sat in the lawn chair next to me, was one of these. He scraped food trays in the central kitchen and lived on a back ward where most of the men wore overalls, and the Techs in their institutional whites rarely wore a smile.

A motorized tram made regular rounds of The State Home, winding through the lanes and avenues that connected its wards and central facilities. The cafeteria was a special destination, a treat for those patients physically able to visit it and fortunate enough to have Techs willing to take them. The tram always stopped where we could watch it load and unload, its canopy-topped cars packed with riders of every description. Techs coaxed groups of their patients on and off; a dozen men walking in single file, each holding onto the belt of the man in front of him because they were blind, a cluster of timid women who clung together and seemed to move as a single unit, a couple holding hands.

And there were the little kids, and teenagers like the Thunderbirds and their female counterparts; all bursting with energy that was barely contained by their medications.

"Dance tonight," Mario said to me one Friday, and I nodded in reply. I knew there was a dance for the patients every Friday, in the gymnasium where I'd taken my entrance exam, but I'd never attended. "Dance tonight," he said again, and I realized that rather than an observation it was a suggestion; he thought I should go. "I like dances," he said, completing for Mario what amounted to a long speech. That sealed the deal.

I met him there that night. The cavernous old gym vibrated to loud rock and roll from a record player and was filled with the sounds of a few hundred patients wheeling their chairs, clapping, dancing, stomping and squealing in delight. Mario had never attended a high school dance; I'd only just stopped going to them. But for a couple of hours, in the dim lights and drumming music, we did what high school guys do at such affairs. We stood together against a back wall and we watched.

CHAPTER SEVEN

MY FOURTH ROTATION was in the post-op wing of the medical-surgical unit, located on the second floor of the imposing old hospital building. It meant that I got to ride up and down in the ancient elevator each day with Clausen, the equally ancient elevator operator. A small man of very few words he sat on a stool in the corner of the elevator car, carefully dressed in a threadbare bellman's uniform, and would ask politely of all who entered, "Department?" Once he noted each he would slide the safety gate closed then work the control handle to guide the car up or down as requested, usually bringing it to a stop almost level with the desired floor.

There were only half a dozen beds in post-op, and patients rarely stayed very long because, as one attendant told me, "They have perfectly good beds waiting for them back on their wards." In many ways it was like a normal hospital; patients recovering from procedures, staff monitoring vital signs, charting, and providing care as needed. "Care as needed" at The State Home might mean washing the walls and everything within them when a patient with projectile emesis spewed a gusher of yellow vomit everywhere. Or restraining the hands of an adult male patient who had just been circumcised but insisted on masturbating anyway. Or tending to female appendectomy patients who showed no signs of recent surgery.

"Yeah, you'll see that sometimes," it was Ponytail who explained it to me. We weren't friends exactly, but our mutual connection with Michelle and the fact that we were both assigned to the hospital made us more than acquaintances. "Bush therapy sometimes leads to an appendectomy, and we do a fair amount of circumcisions on guys who are already circumcised."

I hadn't yet worked on adult ambulatory wards but I'd heard the stories. Sex was no less desired at The State Home than anywhere else, and some patients had a clinical compulsion for it. Techs would sometimes look the other way, or watch, when patient couples were allowed "bush therapy" off the wards; literally sneaking into the bushes to have intercourse. And the rumors of staff actually participating were too plentiful and too specific not to have some basis in fact.

To control their ovulation certain female patients were given an extra vitamin pill along with their daily meds. And certain men received circumcisions that had nothing to do with their foreskins and everything to do with their vas deferens.

But when those measures didn't work an appendectomy would be scheduled just as soon as ward staff detected the pregnancy. Some women had been admitted for more than one.

"You won't find the word sterilization in any of these charts," Ponytail explained when we were on break one day, "but this place used to be famous for it. Back in the thirties the Nazis sent doctors here to learn our techniques. Now it's vitamins, circumcisions and the occasional appendectomy. Same shit, different decade."

There was a small, rarely-used library room on the third floor of the hospital. When post-op was empty I would sometimes go there to study for a test, or just to scan the dusty, disorganized shelves. Medical directories, annual reports, articles and extracts going back sixty years were displayed in no particular order, and among them, glimpses of the institution's unusual past. Here a pamphlet on the therapeutic and social benefits of Eugenics, there a newspaper clipping about polio research. A yellowing proposal for a measles vaccine trial was next to a similar one for hepatitis. With a captive population numbering in the thousands, the place was like a magnet for researchers and experimentalists, and had been since its creation.

"Now it's all about joint replacement research," Ponytail and I were wheeling an unconscious patient who'd just had hip surgery from the O.R. to post-op, one of many similar procedures I'd seen since my rotation started. "Fifteen years ago it was radiation therapy. Somebody had the wild-ass idea that injecting radioactive material into the brains of kids with cerebral palsy might improve their condition. So the administration increased their CP admissions to make sure there was plenty of raw material, and off they went. Only thing is, injecting radiation into people's brains doesn't make them better. It doesn't kill them either, at least not right away. But the morgue and the grave digging Details were a little busier than usual there for a while, or so I heard."

Just the week before, I'd been to the morgue for the first time. It was a low, narrow, unremarkable building next to the fire station. A patient had died on the operating table, an old woman in for a simple procedure, but her heart gave out before they even began. Ponytail said he guessed that the excitement had literally killed her. When I wheeled her body out to the loading dock the van driver asked if I could ride along and help unload; the morgue Tech had apparently called in sick. "I'll have you back in fifteen minutes," he said.

I don't know what I expected. What I saw were file drawers for bodies, just a few. There was the hum of refrigeration, the glare of bare fluorescent bulbs, and a cement floor with a drain in the middle. We pulled out a tray, lifted the old woman's body onto it, and slid it closed. The driver pulled a clipboard from the wall, made a quick notation, and returned it to its hook. That was it.

"What's next for her?" I asked him on the short drive back.

"Next?" he considered for a minute. "If she's got family, maybe they come get her, maybe not. As old as she is, probably not. She might get offered up as a cadaver for medical schools. But after a few days, if there's no takers, I'll get a call. Then I'll drive her up the hill to where a couple of Details will be waiting. First I'll make sure they dug the hole to regulation size, but they're usually pretty good about that.

Then we'll plant her up there, along with all the others."

Chapter Eight

I HAD STARTED my training near the end of one
summer, now another summer was beginning.
The grounds of The State Home, always beautiful,
had taken on a lushness as the days of spring grew
longer, the nights warmer. Sprinklers clicked on
the broad green lawns, and ward windows were
propped open to admit a cooling breeze. In the
evenings, swing shift Techs, to escape the thick
stale air of the dayroom, would frequently take
their patients outside and lounge with them
through the quiet twilight hours.

My final clinical rotation was on a ward for
adult men. It was not a behavior ward exactly,
but a catch all where most of the patients could
walk and most did behave. The ward charge was
a Korean War vet who still carried himself like

a military man; hospital whites stiffly starched, hair cut high and tight. He explained my two case study assignments as he prepared to hand me their charts across his neat metal desk.

"Buck Jones won't give you any trouble, in fact you'll probably want to take him home," High-and-Tight opened the chart to a black and white photo of a young man with Down's syndrome. "Buck was about twenty when this picture was taken, sort of looks like Marlon Brando in *The Wild One*, doesn't he. He's pushing thirty now, which is pretty old for a mongoloid, so he probably doesn't have much time left until his ticker gives out. That's what usually gets them.

To give you more time with Bucky I'm assigning Gerald Keck as your second patient," High-and-Tight slid the chart to me. "You won't be spending much time with Gerald, not if you're smart." I opened the thick folder to a blurred photo of a man with a shaved head, caught in the act of thrashing side to side or straining against some unseen bonds. "Gerald gave me this scar," High-and-Tight extended his right arm and rolled up his sleeve. "Those bite marks are from two years ago, before we had his teeth pulled. You'll help give his meds and feed him if he's calm, but don't ever turn your back on him. I don't want to lose any trainees on my watch.

Carl here, our head Detail, will show you around." I had not heard Carl approach, but turned in my chair to see him standing in the doorway of the small office. A tall, lean man, probably in his forties, Carl wore khakis like a hospital worker and might have passed for one but for the odd, permanent smile that didn't seem to reach his eyes. "Carl, introduce our new trainee to Bucky, and show him where Keck lives."

"Buck, then Keck," Carl said under his breath, then motioned for me to follow as he set off through the ward. The dayroom was lined with hard wooden benches, many with patients laying or rocking on them. "Buck Jones," Carl barked, "are you a high grade, Buck Jones?"

"Buck's a high grade boy," a short man with a big smile and almond shaped eyes looked up from a picture book he was flipping through. "Buck's a good high grade boy, always a high grade boy."

"That's Buck," Carl pointed, "now Keck."

I followed him past the dining hall, and the showers, and into an isolation wing like the one I'd see on my very first ward, where The Thunderbirds had their private bedrooms. "Carl's room," the Detail took a key from his belt and opened the first door we came to. Small, like those I'd seen before, this room one was well appointed, comfortable even, with magazines and a chair, and pinups on the walls. "Carl's," he said again, making sure I understood that it was his, a slight warning in his voice as if he thought I might want what he had. He closed and locked the door very deliberately.

Down the long hallway the other doors we passed were all closed and locked, the rooms unused. "Nobody in this wing but Carl," the Detail said when we came to the last door, "Carl and Keck." He took the same key from his belt, slid it into the lock and reached into his pocket for what looked like a short flashlight, only I knew it wasn't a flashlight.

"For low grade boys," he said, holding the cattle prod up where I could see it.

Then he opened the door.

The room had no furnishings or contents of any kind, not even a mattress. Dried feces were smeared on the wall, as was something darker, blood I guessed. Gerald Keck was stretched out on the floor naked, sleeping or unconscious, I could not tell which. The blood smears had probably come from the open wounds on his scalp. "Head banger," Carl said, "and he smears shit. Low grade."

Keck's body was unlike any I had ever seen. The figure on the floor, even at rest, looked like a big mountain cat poised to strike. His arms and legs, though thin, showed taught bands of muscle that seemed to vibrate through his skin; skin that was a mosaic of bruises and scars, and the paired burn mark signature of the cattle prod's frequent bite. His shaved head, though lumped from repeated blows and displaying a lobotomy scar, was compact and well formed. His nose, by the look of it, had been broken many times.

And Gerald's eyes, when he opened them to stare at us standing there in the doorway, were blue and clear and unflinching.

CHAPTER NINE

CHARTS AT THE State Home, particularly the older ones, often told two stories; the one that was written down and the one that was implied. Buck Jones had been admitted when only a few weeks old, as Baby Boy Jones, parents unknown. Quickly given the nickname Buck in honor of an old cowboy movie star, the baby had grown into a boy on an adolescent ward, then into a man on this one, mostly without incident and largely without notice. I observed that many of the weekly entries in his chart, going back years, were almost identical and written in the same beautifully flowing cursive hand. "Oh, that's old Maggie," one of the Techs explained when I asked about the entries, and he pointed at an elderly patient sitting alone at a table in the dining hall.

"Maggs has been here longer than anybody can remember, nobody knows why. He says it's because he kissed a girl. Could be. But he's got beautiful handwriting. We let him chart most of the time, just copying the last entry into the next if nothing's new, and nothing's hardly ever new with these guys."

Gerald Keck's chart was many times thicker than Buck's and Maggie's handwriting was rarely to be found in it. Born without the ability to speak, Gerald had walked into The State Home in the custody of a marshal when he was ten years old, some twenty-seven years earlier. The boy had a history of fighting, and of running away. With his parents dead, and the grandparents who had raised him in failing health, the authorities stepped in. His initial diagnosis was severe Mental Retardation, though no evidence except his lack of speech was provided to support that claim.

In succeeding years that diagnosis would evolve, and words like mentally unstable, schizophrenic, aggressive and violent appeared with increasing frequency. But Gerald's core behavior did not change; he still fought, he still ran away. There were many reports of injuries, his and those he inflicted on others. And he had a standing order for restraints; cuffing and belting as needed. But as the boy got older and stronger, and as nothing seemed to work, more strident measures were employed to keep him under control.

First it was electro convulsive therapy. Proven successful on many violent patients, in Gerald's case it had virtually no lasting effect regardless of how frequently it was administered. Lobotomy was next, but the result was the same, and the violence and compulsion to run only seemed to increase. Thorazine showed promise when they first prescribed it, but as he developed a tolerance, larger and larger doses had less and less impact. If left unattended with others he would attack them. If left an opening he would try to escape.

An orthopedic surgeon finally controlled the latter behavior. Listed as a procedure to correct hip dysfunction, Gerald had walked, under restraint, into the hospital on his own two feet. After the operation he would never run, or even stand on them again.

I TOOK HIGH-and-Tight's advice about Gerald, at least in the beginning. Buck Jones was fun to be with, like an older kid brother. We'd walk to the cafeteria for ice cream, or explore the creek that ran through the grounds; skipping stones and catching frogs. My clinical project was to help improve his personal grooming. With some clothes from the donation bin, a little practice using an electric razor and a fair amount of goop for his unruly hair, we made good progress.

Gerald Keck I only saw twice a day, for morning meds and then again at his mid-day feeding. Each encounter was the same. Three of us would enter his room together; Carl, a Tech from the regular staff, and I. Carl would restrain his hands, sometimes actually standing on his wrists to hold them down. I would hold his legs, rendered useless by the surgery that had crippled him but still surprisingly strong in my grip. The Tech would hold his head and try to force down the meds or the food, careful not to get a finger clamped between Gerald's toothless but still menacing gums.

Then one day Carl got called away as we were about to feed Gerald. A patient had messed himself, a common occurrence on the ward, and he needed hosing down in the shower room. Carl took special delight in using the hose; I'd watched him when Buck had an accident one day. He would spray the water playfully sometimes, then not so playfully, then he'd bring the hose close to the man's backside in a pantomime of sex, and he'd laugh, and he'd laugh.

With only two of us there, the Tech said he'd hold Gerald's hands down if I was willing to shovel in the food. "No offence, but when there isn't a trainee available this is how we usually do it", he explained. "The legs aren't much of a threat anyway", he said, and though I'd felt the strength in them every day with my own hands I agreed to give it a try.

Gerald didn't spring at us when we opened the door as he sometimes did when Carl was present. He never cowered or shrank away, it was not in his nature, but sometimes he was more wary than others. Not so this time. We entered the room and he sat upright in the middle of the floor, his legs curled under him, his hands relaxed at his sides. The Tech walked behind him, taking hold of his wrists but not roughly, and Gerald did not resist.

The food was some sort of ground mush; it might have been meat and potatoes at one point. I knelt at Gerald's side, took a spoonful from the metal tray and raised it to his mouth. Never looking at it, only looking at me, he opened wide and took what I offered. In a few minutes the tray was empty and the plastic cup of water, and the one of juice as well. Sometimes after feeding Gerald, Carl would bring the hose, and mop, and cattle prod to clean up the mess. This time I wiped his mouth with a cloth towel, not thinking how close I was coming to his jaws. But he didn't snap at me. He just lay back down on the bare concrete floor and watched as we left.

Over the following days and weeks Gerald and I repeated this ritual frequently, and began some others. He wasn't allowed a mattress because he tore them up immediately, and any blanket quickly became shreds in his powerful, claw like hands. But when I asked High-and Tight for permission to try a blanket again, as part of my clinical study, he agreed. When it lasted one day, then another, then a week, I got permission to try some other things.

Gerald could go to the toilet when he was allowed the opportunity, but it was not a simple process. Employing a long pole with a restraining neck collar at the end, Carl would walk behind Gerald as he crawled down the hallway and back. But when Carl was busy elsewhere, or wanted an excuse to use his hose and other tools, he'd let Gerald go on the floor of his cell.

High-and-Tight was more than skeptical when I asked if I could introduce a diaper. "He'll try to put our eyes out with the pins," he said, "or rip the thing into a rope and strangle one of us." But he'd noticed the changes, small as they were, and he was curious to see what would happen. "Use the smallest safety pins you can find," he said, "and if he swallows them you can dig them out of his shit."

But he didn't swallow them. When I put the diaper on him that first time, a big course thing half the size of a table cloth, I was nervous and he was nervous, I could see it in his eyes. But he let me clean him up, with a washrag not a hose. He even raised his body slightly so I could slide the diaper under him.

Perhaps I was more fascinated by him than afraid of him, and he knew that. Or perhaps he was just tired after so much struggle for so many years. Whatever the reason, Gerald seemed calmer when I was around. All the Techs noticed it. Carl noticed it.

I had taken to dividing my time on the ward pretty evenly between my two case study patients, joking and watching TV with Buck, and sometimes just watching Gerald. There was a small exercise yard at the back of the ward; fenced and locked, but open to the air and with a nice view of the hills behind the grounds. One corner was sectioned off, like a dog run almost, and for an hour or so every day I was allowed to take Gerald there and sit with him. The first few times High-and-Tight made me use the restraining collar, but eventually I was able to just walk him there, out the back door and into the yard. I discovered that he liked to roll a ball, so I'd sit with him in the little dog run, roll the ball to him, and he'd roll it back.

There and back, there and back.

CHAPTER TEN

"YOU SEE THESE boots?" it was the barber making his monthly haircutting rounds. "Some people might call them kick boots, I call them Keck boots," he said, pausing in his work on Gerald's hair to turn his foot this way and that so I could see the heels and the sharp pointed toes. "Three years ago your boy Keck here came at me for no reason. Yeah, I nicked one of these lumps on his scalp, but that didn't mean he had to throw me against a counter and crack three vertebrae. Now I can't stand more than ten minutes at a time. You know what the means for a barber?"

The man was in his fifties, with a slight build and a narrow face, and fear masked as anger trembling in his voice. "It means if I don't cut hair at The State Home, I don't cut hair at all.

Carl tells me you've gotten friendly with Keck, good for you," he said. "But you'll be off this ward in a couple of weeks, maybe even transfer to another hospital when you get your license. That's a bright future ahead, good for you my young friend. Me, I'm not going anywhere. Keck saw to that. And he's not going anywhere either, are you Gerald? If he ever comes at me again, and I know he will, I'll take these boots to him, bad back or not."

Gerald was strapped into a chair, Carl holding him in place with the restraining collar and pole, while the barber mowed over his scalp with noisy electric clippers.

THE LAST WEEK of training was all classroom time, which meant that work on our clinical units and with our case studies was done; there was no need to go back. I'd given Buck a baseball cap and a bottle of aftershave as a going away present on that last day. He gave me a big generous hug and a smile in return. I couldn't think of what to give Gerald, or what he might be allowed to keep, so I just sat with him for an hour and hoped he couldn't sense that things were about to change.

A couple of days later I had an idea; I could give him his own ball. They might not let him keep it, but I could give it to him at least.

It was just coming on dusk when I got to the ward. The swing shift Tech in charge recognized me, and loaned me his key so I could unlock Gerald's room and take him to the yard out back. "Watch out for him", the Tech said, and I assured him that I would.

"Watch out for him", I was thinking to myself as I walked onto the isolation wing. Carl was in his room, his door open, and he looked up at me as I passed. Was it my imagination, or was there something like triumph in his eyes?

The door to Gerald's room swung open, and it was just like that first time again. No blanket, no diaper, and the dark smears of feces and blood on the walls. He was stretched out on the floor, muscles tensed, eyes alert, a cat ready spring. Then he saw the ball.

I stepped back from the door and he followed me into the hallway, leaving a thin trail of slime on the floor behind him. Out the backdoor we went, and into the little fenced yard where we had spent so much time. I sat on one side, he on the other, and I rolled him the ball.

It was a beautiful evening, clear and warm, and ripe with the promise of things sensed but unseen. As we rolled the ball my eyes drifted to twilight landscape above The State Home. I imagined the creeks and the meadows and the sheltered hollows up there, where patients sometimes ran away, and sometimes didn't come back. I imagined, then I noticed that the ball had stopped coming.

Gerald had followed my gaze. He too was staring up into the purpling hills.

Then he did the most extraordinary thing I have ever seen.

Looping his fingers in the chain-link fence he pulled himself slowly erect. Electric shock, a lobotomy, and drugs strong enough to kill most men hadn't stopped him. Neither had the surgeon's knife.

Gerald Keck was on his feet and he was ready to run.

I had the key in my hand. The back gate was only a few yards away, and beyond that the creek and then the hills. He could survive up there. If they hadn't killed him yet he could survive any-where. There were caves he could shelter in, and a lake, and he could forage for food. "Watch out for him," the Tech had told me just a few minutes before.

"Watch out for him."

CHAPTER ELEVEN

DID I UNLOCK the gate?

You know the answer.

Would I do it now if I could go back?

I honestly don't know.

That was forty-three years ago. I passed my licensing exam and worked night shift as a Psych Tech for almost a year, assigned to a ward that housed many of the very first patients I'd met at The State Home back when I was still in high school. We didn't make crape paper flowers or square dance anymore. But I did sing to them in the mornings as I hoisted them, cranky and often dripping urine, from their beds.

I'd been on the job about six months when word came around that Gerald Keck had run away. Escaped to the hills was the rumor, and I wanted to believe it was true. But I knew better. Carl, or the barber, or the place itself had finally gotten to him. Gerald had escaped all right, but to an unmarked hole up on the hillside, along with all the others.

I left The State Home behind me finally, or tried to, but I never left the valley where it nestles among the hills. Family and career and more good fortune than anyone has a right to expect have come my way, but still those early days linger in my mind.

The place itself is mostly closed now, only a few hundred patients where once there were thousands. And those hundreds of acres stretching to the ridge above it have become a wilderness park, accessed by hiking trails that lead from the valley floor all the way to the summit. I run there frequently, sometimes with friends, but often by myself. There really are creeks and caves, and dark forest hollows where the light barely penetrates.

Do I still look for God, like my old friend suggested, as I slowly jog those mountain paths? I don't think so. I look for the breathtaking vistas, and the quiet glades, and the sun filtering down through the trees. I see deer and wild turkey, the occasional fox, even a mountain lion once; moving low and sleek as it crossed the trail in front of me.

I don't think I'm looking for myself either, not really. I know who I am, and I'm at peace with that.

But I look just the same, when a twig snaps or leaves rustle, or I hear the sound of movement through the tall, thick grass.

I stop, and I turn, and I look for Gerald Keck.

I look for Gerald.

The End

13721116R00050

Made in the USA
San Bernardino, CA
02 August 2014